C000215414

The Best of
Alex
2002

Charles Peattie
& Russell Taylor

Masterley Publishing

The Best of
Alex
2002

Copyright © 2001 - 2002 Charles Peattie and Russell Taylor

The right of Charles Peattie and Russell Taylor to be identified as the Author of the Work has been asserted by them in accordance with the Copyright, Designs and Patents Act 1988.

First published in 2002 by
MASTERLEY PUBLISHING

All rights reserved. No part of this publication may be reproduced, stored in a retrieval system, or transmitted, in any form or by any means without the prior written permission of the publisher, nor be otherwise circulated in any form of binding or cover other than that in which it is published and without a similar condition being imposed on the subsequent purchaser.

Design and digital artwork by
OCEAN Digital Media.com

Every day asset owners and financial professionals, like Alex, look to FTSE for the
index tools to support their international investment strategies. FTSE is delighted to sponsor
the Best of Alex 2002 and hope that you enjoy it as much as we did.
www.ftse.com.

MondoVisione, publisher of the Handbook of World Stock, Derivative and
Commodity Exchanges, is pleased to support once more that other essential
handbook of the financial community, the Alex annual.

FOREWORD

On September 11th 2001 we were on our summer break and so there were no Alex cartoon strips in the Telegraph that week. This meant we were spared from having to reflect the one subject everyone was talking about but which it was also impossible to be funny on . By the time Alex was back in the paper the initial horror had receded and recognisable City-type perspectives on the implications of events were beginning to develop.

But, as with all major shocks and sea-changes when the world seems a more frightening place, it's a time when people maybe begin to call into question how important are all the things in our lives that are just shallow and ephemeral and cynical and trivial and frivolous.

The answer is: even more vitally important than ever, probably.

So welcome to the new Alex book. A big thank you to all our moles in the city (you know who you are) for all the behind the scenes gossip and the lunches too. And here's to next year being a bit easier to joke about.

Charles Peattie and Russell Taylor.

Alex PEATTIE + TAYLOR

THE HARDCASTLE A.G.M. TODAY IS GOING TO BE WORSE THAN EVER. YOU KNOW HOW PROUD THE OLD BOY IS OF HIS COMPANY...

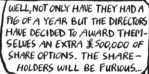

WELL, NOT ONLY HAVE THEY HAD A PIG OF A YEAR BUT THE DIRECTORS HAVE DECIDED TO AWARD THEMSELVES AN EXTRA £500,000 OF SHARE OPTIONS. THE SHAREHOLDERS WILL BE FURIOUS...

THEN I HAVE TO STAND UP AND ASK HARDCASTLE A TAME QUESTION ABOUT THE FORTHCOMING YEAR. HE'LL SPOUT THE USUAL ROSE-TINTED GUFF AND EVERYONE WILL THINK I'M A TOTAL SYCOPHANT...

I'M HAPPY TO DO IT, CLIVE.

YOU ARE? YOU'RE ON...

IN ANSWER TO THE GENTLEMAN'S QUESTION: OUR PROFITS ARE LOOKING BAD, SALES ARE SLUMPING, MARKET SHARE DIMINISHING...

THE LOWER HE CAN GET HIS SHARE PRICE THE MORE OPTIONS HE GETS...

HARDCASTLE A.G.M.

Alex PEATTIE + TAYLOR

WELL, TIM, AS A BONA FIDE AUSTRALIAN CLIENT YOU WERE LIKE GOLD DUST TO THOSE OF US WHO WENT OUT THERE FOR THE LIONS TOUR...

email: alex-cartoon@etgate.co.uk

YES AND WE WERE DELIGHTED TO HAVE BEEN ABLE TO REPAY THE FAVOUR BY INVITING YOU OVER HERE TO LORDS FOR THE ASHES TEST...

AH, RUPERT. HAVE YOU MET TIM DANIELS?

TIM! WELL I NEVER... YOU'RE LOOKING REMARKABLY SVELTE, I MUST SAY. HOWEVER DID YOU LOSE ALL THAT WEIGHT?

ER...EXCUSE ME? I'M SORRY, I DON'T THINK WE'VE MET..

TRUE, BUT ACCORDING TO THE EXPENSES CLAIMS PUT IN BY MY DEPARTMENT, YOU ATE SIX MEALS A DAY LAST WEEK...

Alex PEATTIE + TAYLOR

AH... THERE YOU ARE, PETER... WHAT ARE YOU DOING HERE IN BUSINESS CLASS, ALEX? YOU HAD ECONOMY TICKETS.

email: alex-cartoon@etgate.co.uk

I MANAGED TO GET MYSELF UPGRADED. IT'S A PIECE OF CAKE IF ONE ADOPTS THE RIGHT PSYCHOLOGICAL APPROACH WITH THE STAFF AT CHECK-IN...

AND IT HELPS IF ONE'S TRAVELLING COMPANION IS ABLE TO INFLUENCE THEIR JUDGEMENT BY SHOWING A BIT OF LEG... WITH A GENEROUS GLIMPSE OF STOCKING...

TAP TAP

ER... BUT, ALEX, THE CHECK-IN STAFF ARE ALL WOMEN...

CAN I TAKE THIS SURGICAL STOCKING OFF NOW, ALEX? IT'S KILLING ME...

WITH THE AIRLINES TERRIFIED OF DEEP VEIN THROMBOSIS IT'S USEFUL TO SUGGEST YOU SUFFER FROM VARICOSE VEINS...

Alex PEATTIE + TAYLOR

HEY, ALEX, I'VE GOT MY CLUBS HERE... ARE WE ON FOR A GAME LATER?

SORRY, TONY, I CAN'T DO IT TODAY...

email: alex-cartoon@etgate.co.uk

≡SIGH≡ YOU CITY BOYS ARE NO FUN ANY MORE... THESE DAYS YOU NEVER HAVE A CHANCE TO FIT IN A ROUND OF GOLF WITH AN OLD SCHOOL CHUM LIKE ME.

I'M SORRY, TONY...

I MEAN, YOU KNOW I'D LOVE TO BUT...

OH NEVER MIND... I WAS JUST CALLING ON THE OFF-CHANCE, ALEX... AND I'LL TAKE THIS AS A TESTAMENT TO HOW BUSY THE WORLD OF BANKING IS AT THE MOMENT...

BECAUSE NORMALLY A FEW OF YOUR CITY CLIENTS DROP OUT AT THE LAST MINUTE AND YOU CALL ME UP...

SADLY NO ONE'S GOT ANY WORK ON AND WE'RE CHOC-A-BLOCK HERE.

MEGABANK GOLF DAY

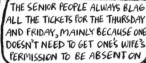

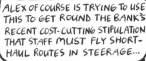

Alex PEATTIE + TAYLOR

I UNDERSTAND THAT THE BANK IS BEING SUED BY DISGRUNTLED INVESTORS WHO LOST THEIR SHIRTS ON INTERNET STOCKS...

THESE PEOPLE ARE CLAIMING THAT THEY WERE GIVEN MISLEADING AND SELF-MOTIVATED ADVICE BY MEGA-BANK ANALYSTS WHO WERE TIPPING THE STOCKS. YOU'RE OUR LAWYER, NIGEL. WHAT'S OUR LEGAL POSITION?

WELL, RUPERT, ALL THE REQUIRED DISCLAIMERS AND CAVEATS WERE ISSUED AT THE TIME WARNING INVESTORS THAT SHARE PRICES CAN GO DOWN AS WELL AS UP... OUR ANALYSTS DID NOTHING ILLEGAL...

THEY DIDN'T?

BLAST... IT WOULD HAVE BEEN HANDY TO HAVE AN EXCUSE TO SACK THEM ALL WITHOUT ENTITLEMENT TO COMPENSATION...

SO... ANY OTHER IDEAS AS TO HOW TO GET THE HEADCOUNT DOWN?

email: alex-cartoon@etgate.co.uk

Alex PEATTIE + TAYLOR

IT NOW SEEMS THE TERRORISTS BEHIND THE SEPTEMBER 11th ATTACKS MAY HAVE BEEN MANIPULATING THE FINANCIAL MARKETS...

GETTING WALL STREET TO FINANCE ITS OWN DESTRUCTION... AS ONE HEARS MORE DETAILS THIS WHOLE BUSINESS JUST BECOMES MORE AND MORE BEWILDERING AND UNREAL...

AND THE MEDIA OVER HERE HAVE A LOT TO ANSWER FOR. I CAN'T BELIEVE THE WAY THE NEWS PROGRAMMES GIVE AIRTIME TO THESE DREADFUL FUNDAMENTALISTS...

I THINK THIS ONE'S ACTUALLY A CHARTIST, PENNY... BUT ANALYSTS ARE INCOMPREHENSIBLE AT THE BEST OF TIMES...

BASICALLY THE TERRORISTS WOULD THEN HAVE SOLD SHORT TERM CALLS ON THE DAX...

email: alex-cartoon@etgate.co.uk

Alex PEATTIE + TAYLOR

THE LATEST RUMOUR IS THAT BIN LADEN'S TERRORIST NETWORK WERE TRADING STOCK PORTFOLIOS AND PLAYING THE FINANCIAL MARKETS...

WEIRD, ISN'T IT?

I GUESS WE CAN TRY TO TRACE THEIR ASSETS AND FIND OUT WHERE THEIR MONEY IS AND DEAL WITH THEM THAT WAY... BUT CAN WE EVER WIPE THEM OUT COMPLETELY?

WELL, CLIVE...

WE'RE TALKING ABOUT FANATICS WHO DON'T CARE WHAT HAPPENS TO THEM... WHO ARE BENT ON DEFYING WESTERN CAPITALISM... EACH OF WHOM IS PREPARED TO PAY THE HIGHEST PRICE ON BEHALF OF THEIR CAUSE...

DOTCOM SHARES?!! OKAY!! I'LL BUY SOME OF THOSE!

MY BROKER SAYS PILE INTO LEISURE STOCKS NOW! I'M GONNA GO FOR IT!!

HEY! TELECOMS ARE CR*PPING OUT! LET'S SHIP 'EM IN!! YO!!

...SO, YES, BASICALLY...

email: alex-cartoon@etgate.co.uk

Alex PEATTIE + TAYLOR

WELL, CLIVE, YOU AND I KNOW THAT WE'RE LOOKING AT ONE OF THE CLASSIC INDICATORS THAT MARKS THE ONSET OF A RECESSION...

YES, ALL OF US OLDER PEOPLE RECOGNISE IT. ROBIN'S JUST ABOUT THE ONLY PERSON IN THE OFFICE WHO'S NOT LOOKING GRIM-FACED...

THAT'S UNDERSTANDABLE.

AFTER ALL, HE'S NEW TO THE CITY. HE'S NEVER LIVED THROUGH A RECESSION BEFORE. HE HAS NO IDEA OF THE DEPRESSING PREDICTABILITY WITH WHICH THESE THINGS COME ROUND...

"PEDIGREE CHUM HAS GONE BUST AND CALLED IN THE RETRIEVERS"

HA HA HA...

THAT OLD CHESTNUT HAS BEEN TROTTED OUT IN EVERY DOWNTURN SINCE 1987...

GOOD ONE!

e-mail joke

19

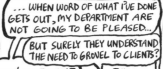

Alex PEATTIE + TAYLOR

WHAT'S THIS, GRAHAM? A 100-PAGE RESEARCH NOTE ON TECH STOCKS? PLEASE DON'T WASTE MY TIME...

SO JUST BECAUSE THE SECTOR I FOLLOW HAPPENS TO BE IN THE DOLDRUMS, WITH NO ONE SHOWING THE REMOTEST INTEREST, I'M EXPECTED TO WRITE NOTHING AT ALL, IS THAT IT?

THAT WOULD SEEM SENSIBLE... YES.

WELL, ALEX, EVEN IF NO CLIENTS WANT TO DEAL, PRODUCING RESEARCH HELPS TO RAISE MY PROFILE AS AN ANALYST, GET MY NAME ABOUT, REMIND PEOPLE OF MY EXISTENCE...

GRAHAM MOORE? I THOUGHT WE SACKED HIM MONTHS AGO... I MUST REMEMBER TO DO IT THIS AFTERNOON...

Alex PEATTIE + TAYLOR

IN A COST-CUTTING ENVIRONMENT IT'S USEFUL WHEN STAFF RESIGN VOLUNTARILY RATHER THAN HAVE TO BE MADE REDUNDANT...

HUMAN RESOURCES DIRECTOR

THAT'S WHY I WANT TO ENCOURAGE A MOOD OF PESSIMISM AND GLOOM. BUT AT SOME POINT ACTIVE JOB CUTS WILL NEED TO BE MADE. THE QUESTION IS: FROM WHERE?

DON'T LOOK AT MY DIVISION, RUPERT...

WE IN HUMAN RESOURCES MAY NOT ACTUALLY MAKE PROFITS BUT DON'T FORGET THAT WE PLAY A VITAL SUPPORT ROLE FOR THE BANK'S ENTIRE STAFF BASE...

TRUE, SHELLEY. YOUR DEPARTMENT CAN BE OF GREAT USE...

I HEAR THEY'VE LET FIFTY H.R. PEOPLE 60...

IF THE BANK'S DISPENSING WITH THEIR JOBS WHAT DOES THAT SAY ABOUT THE FUTURE OF OURS?

GLOOM

Alex PEATTIE + TAYLOR

WHAT'S GOING ON? THESE PEOPLE ARE SUPPOSED TO BE STOCK-BROKERS. SO WHY AREN'T THEY DOING ANY WORK?

FRANKLY, NONE OF THEIR CLIENTS WANT TO DEAL IN THE CURRENT CLIMATE SO THERE'S NO POINT IN CALLING ANYONE.

I AM AWARE THAT BUSINESS IS BAD WHICH IS WHY I DO NOT WANT MY STAFF DOING NOTHING...

NOW I WANT TO SEE THOSE PEOPLE ON THE PHONE ALL DAY LONG...

WELL YOU CAN INSIST ON THAT IF YOU LIKE BUT ALL THEY'LL DO IS PHONE THEIR FELLOW BROKERS FOR A GOSSIP...

PRECISELY... WHICH SHOULD HOPEFULLY UPDATE THEM ON THE LATEST RUMOURS ABOUT REDUNDANCIES ELSEWHERE... IT'S ALWAYS HANDY TO GET THEIR BONUS EXPECTATIONS DOWN...

Alex PEATTIE + TAYLOR

THERE HAVE BEEN FEARS THAT THIS YEAR'S OCTOBER CLUB CHARITY DINNER WON'T RAISE AS MUCH AS PREVIOUS OCCASIONS...

WITH RECESSION BECKONING AND JOBS AT RISK, PEOPLE ARE BEGINNING TO FEEL NERVOUS... THOUGH OBVIOUSLY WE SENIOR PEOPLE ARE LESS SUSCEPTIBLE TO FINANCIAL UNCERTAINTIES...

WHICH IS WHY WE HAVE AN OBLIGATION TO PROVIDE AN EXAMPLE. AFTER ALL, THIS CHARITY AUCTION GIVES US THE CHANCE TO HELP THOSE LESS FORTUNATE THAN OURSELVES...

YES...

...OUR UNDERLINGS WHOSE BONUSES WE'LL BE ASSIGNING... LET'S HOPE THEY'RE GETTING THE MESSAGE...

NONE OF THE BOSSES HAVE BID FOR ANYTHING ALL EVENING...

I KNOW... THE BONUS POOL MUST BE SERIOUSLY EMPTY...

GLOOM

email: alex-cartoon@etgate.co.uk

27

29

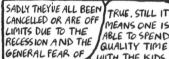

Alex PEATTIE + TAYLOR

SOME PEOPLE THINK THAT 360° APPRAISALS WERE ONLY INVENTED TO GIVE US IN H.R. A REASON TO EXIST...

HUMAN RESOURCES

AND EVERYONE GRUMBLES ABOUT HAVING TO FIND TEN COLLEAGUES TO WRITE A REPORT ON THEM, BUT THE END PRODUCT IS A VITAL TOOL FOR MANAGEMENT, FOR OBVIOUS REASONS...

I SUPPOSE SOLICITING A WIDE RANGE OF PERSONAL OPINIONS HELPS BOSSES COME TO DECISIONS BY PROVIDING THEM WITH A BALANCED AND OBJECTIVE OVERVIEW OF EACH INDIVIDUAL STAFF MEMBER.

OH DEAR...YOU'VE STILL GOT A LOT TO LEARN.

NO... A LOAD OF CONFLICTING OPINIONS JUSTIFIES BOSSES DOING WHATEVER THEY'D ALREADY DECIDED TO DO...

OK..ROGERS IS ON THE REDUNDANCY LIST, SO FIND SOMEONE WHO SAID SOMETHING BAD ABOUT HIM...

Alex PEATTIE + TAYLOR

IN THE MODERN COST-CUTTING OFFICE ENVIRONMENT E-MAIL AND VOICEMAIL HAVE BEEN IMPORTANT INNOVATIONS...

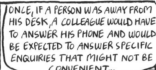

ONCE, IF A PERSON WAS AWAY FROM HIS DESK, A COLLEAGUE WOULD HAVE TO ANSWER HIS PHONE AND WOULD BE EXPECTED TO ANSWER SPECIFIC ENQUIRIES THAT MIGHT NOT BE CONVENIENT...

IT'S FAR MORE CONDUCIVE TO THE SMOOTH RUNNING OF THE BANK IF THE CALLER IS ABLE TO LEAVE AN E-MAIL OR VOICEMAIL DIRECTLY FOR THE INDIVIDUAL IN QUESTION...

YES...

...IT TAKES LONGER FOR WORD TO GET OUT WHEN WE'VE SACKED SOMEONE...

WHEN MESSAGES AREN'T RETURNED, CALLERS TEND TO ASSUME THE PERSON IS JUST ON HOLIDAY...

Alex PEATTIE + TAYLOR

IT'S A FAIRLY UNUSUAL INNOVATION TO HAVE A HOROSCOPE PAGE IN A BANK'S IN-HOUSE MAGAZINE SURELY, RUPERT?

NOT REALLY...

IN INVESTMENT BANKING WE'RE PRIMARILY CONCERNED WITH THE PRECISE SCIENTIFIC BUSINESS OF MAKING MONEY BUT THERE'S ALWAYS ROOM FOR THE LESS EXACT DISCIPLINES TOO...

NOT LEAST OF WHICH IS THAT TIME-HONOURED, MUCH-PRACTISED ART WHICH OFFERS GUIDANCE TO FUTURE EVENTS THROUGH VEILED PRONOUNCE-MENTS THAT MAY STRIKE A CHORD IN THE READER...

ASTROLOGY?

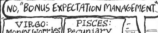

NO, "BONUS EXPECTATION MANAGEMENT"...

VIRGO: Money worries resurface This month...

PISCES: Pecuniary uncertainties lie ahead...

LEO: Saturn in your 4th house will have an adverse effect on your finances

---

Alex PEATTIE + TAYLOR

ECONOMICALLY THE FAR EAST STILL DOES NOT SEEM TO HAVE EXTRACTED ITSELF FROM THE DOLDRUMS...

THANK GOODNESS WE NEVER WENT BACK INTO THOSE MARKETS AFTER WE PULLED OUT WHOLE-SALE FOLLOWING THE MOST RECENT DOWNTURN OUT THERE.

IT MEANS THAT AT A TIME WHEN COSTS ARE ALREADY TIGHT, THE BANK WILL NOT HAVE TO RISK EXPOSURE TO A REPEAT OF THE FINANCIALLY RUINOUS EVENTS OF 1998... THE COLLAPSE OF THE ASIAN MARKETS?

NO, THE LAST WORLD CUP AND THE EXORBITANT EXPENSES CLAIMS IT PRODUCED... I'M BANNING ALL CLIENT ENTERTAINMENT AT JAPAN AND KOREA 2002...

35

Alex PEATTIE + TAYLOR

I'M SO PLEASED TO SEE THAT MORALE IN THE OFFICE IS GOOD THIS JANUARY...

THERE'S A PALPABLE AIR OF CONTENTMENT AROUND. THAT'S A REFLECTION OF HOW WELL THE CITY IS DOING AT THE MOMENT.

SO OFTEN THE START OF A NEW YEAR CAN INDUCE A GENERAL MOOD OF PESSIMISM WITH PEOPLE FEELING APATHETIC, UNMOTIVATED AND VAGUELY DESPONDENT...

...BECAUSE HALF OF THEIR COLLEAGUES HAVE LEFT TO GO TO NEW JOBS...?

EXACTLY. BUT THINGS ARE SO DIRE THIS YEAR THAT THERE AREN'T ANY JOBS FOR ANYONE TO GO TO...

email: alex-cartoon@etgate.co.uk

Alex PEATTIE + TAYLOR

TOBY, IT'S ALEX MASTERLEY PHONING TO WISH YOU A HAPPY NEW YEAR... AND NO DOUBT GET SOME BUSINESS OFF ME...

WELL, IT WOULDN'T GO AMISS... IT'S NO SECRET THAT LAST YEAR WAS NOT A GOOD ONE FOR US... I'M SURE I'M NOT THE ONLY ONE OF YOUR CLIENTS TO HAVE DETECTED THAT FACT...

WHEN THE QUESTION OF MY GIVING YOU SOME BUSINESS AROSE LAST MONTH I WELL RECALL THE PLEADING TONE IN YOUR VOICE - THE SHEER DESPERATION SHOWING IN THE WORDS YOU SAID TO ME...

"NO, PLEASE . NOT UNDER ANY CIRCUMSTANCES..." I WOULDN'T HAVE WANTED IT TO GET SWALLOWED UP IN THE BLACK HOLE OF LAST YEAR'S LOSSES...

email: alex-cartoon@etgate.co.uk

Alex PEATTIE + TAYLOR

2002 DOESN'T LOOK ANY BETTER THAN LAST YEAR. IT'S STILL IMPOSSIBLE TO INTEREST ANY OF OUR CLIENTS IN DOING ANY DEALS...

AND AT THE SAME TIME WE'RE HAVING TO ENDURE A VICIOUS REGIME OF STRINGENT AND PETTY COST-CUTTING IMPOSED BY HEAD OFFICE...

AH... BUT HERE'S ALEX, BACK FROM A MEETING WITH MR HARDCASTLE AND LOOKING QUITE PLEASED WITH HIMSELF... HOW WAS IT, ALEX? FRUITFUL...? "FRUITFUL"? I'D SAY SO...

..HARDCASTLE DIDN'T SHOW UP SO I SNAFFLED THESE FROM THE MEETING ROOM... WOW!... GUAVAS, LYCHEES, PASSION-FRUIT... ITEMS NOW ONLY SUPPLIED FOR EXTERNAL CLIENT MEETINGS...

email: alex-cartoon@etgate.co.uk

Alex PEATTIE + TAYLOR

THIS "HABITAT FOR HUMANITY" SCHEME GIVES US BANKERS A CHANCE TO PUT SOMETHING BACK INTO THE COMMUNITY...

BUT, MORE IMPORTANTLY, IN SPENDING A DAY OR TWO ACTUALLY BUILDING HOUSES FOR UNDERPRIVILEGED FAMILIES OUR CHAPS GET TO UNDERTAKE TASKS FAR REMOVED FROM THEIR DAY JOBS AT THE BANK...

PERSONALLY I FIND IT VERY SATISFYING BEING ABLE TO DO SOMETHING WHICH CAN - IN THE MOST GENUINE SENSE OF THE WORD - BE TERMED "CONSTRUCTIVE"...

WHAT, CONSTRUCTIVE DISMISSAL?

EXACTLY. I'VE HAD FOSTER ON THIS DETAIL FOR THREE WEEKS. LET'S HOPE HE GETS THE HINT AND RESIGNS...

email: alex-cartoon@etgate.co.uk

43

Alex — PEATTIE + TAYLOR

It's going to be a glorious festival come the first week in June.

Well, yes and no, Clive...

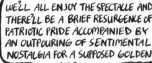

We'll all enjoy the spectacle and there'll be a brief resurgence of patriotic pride accompanied by an outpouring of sentimental nostalgia for a supposed golden age...

But in the end we'll be paying homage to a symbol of our nation which has over the last 30 years consistently discredited itself and is now no more than a joke in most people's eyes...

THE MONARCHY?!

Oh, sorry. I thought you were talking about the England football team...

If anyone mentions 1966 again....

Alex

The recent sex discrimination court case has highlighted the issue of women in banks...

Now, I respect and value my female staff, but at times like this with business hard to come by, it's MEN I want in my trading room...

Frankly when the going gets tough it's the testosterone flowing in their veins that gives them something that women rarely have...

A lot of illegal porn on their computer hard disks...?

Exactly. It makes them so much easier to fire...

Alex

What I like about you, Alex, is that you understand the power of the press...

More wine, Dominic?

After all, investment banks spend huge amounts on P.R. events designed to bolster their image, but in times of cutbacks, money for such things may not be forthcoming...

You however realise that you simply have to treat a financial journalist like me to a decent lunch and I'll give your bank the required coverage in tomorrow's paper.

I see we've been slagged off in today's Bugle...

Ah! Good old Dominic. Right, now's the time to get that skinflint Rupert to authorise a much-needed profile-raising golf day...

Alex

So Alex whisked you off for a surprise weekend break in Venice?

Yes. Just the two of us. It was so romantic...

You know, sometimes I feel I'm being a bit harsh on Alex when I think he's just obsessed with his job and his status within the business world...

I know it's been very stressful for him at work of late with poor levels of business and general cutbacks. It was so sweet he still found time to think of me...

So when did you realise that, due to lack of business travel, you were 120 points short of the total needed to keep your gold frequent flyer card?

5 minutes before I decided to book the Venice trip...

44

46

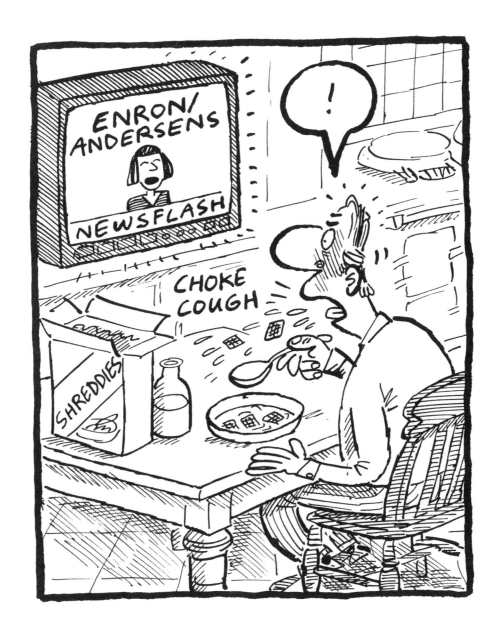

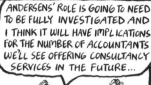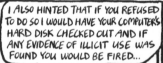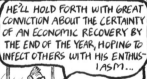

49

ARE WE HAVING TO QUEUE, RUPERT?

FOOLISHLY I OMITTED TO BOOK A TABLE, DONALD...

I JUST ASSUMED THAT DUE TO THE RECESSIONARY CLIMATE IN THE CITY, RESTAURANTS WOULDN'T BE BUSY. HOWEVER, IT SEEMS THAT BECAUSE NO ONE'S GOT ANY WORK ON, LUNCHING IS BACK IN FASHION...

THIS IS AN INTOLERABLE SITUATION WHERE SENIOR DIRECTORS OF INVESTMENT BANKS ARE UNABLE TO GET A TABLE AT A RESTAURANT. SURELY SOMETHING CAN BE DONE?

IT IS BEING DONE...

WE'RE FIRING 3,000 PEOPLE ON MONDAY...

GOOD NEWS. OUR OWN "OPERATION LONG KNIVES" WILL ALSO SHORTLY BE UNDER WAY...

email: alex-cartoon@etgate.co.uk

WELL, CLIVE, HERE WE ARE IN THE 21ST CENTURY AND THE BANKING WORLD HAS CHANGED BEYOND ALL RECOGNITION...

TO THINK WE SCOFFED AT YOUNG ROBIN A COUPLE OF YEARS BACK WHEN HE PREDICTED THE INTERNET WOULD REVOLUTIONISE OUR EVERYDAY WORKING LIVES...

YET FOR BOTH INFORMATION DELIVERY AND COMMERCIAL TRANSACTIONS IT HAS ALREADY BECOME AN INTEGRAL PART OF THE NEW MILLENNIAL BUSINESS ENVIRONMENT...

...WHERE NO ONE'S GOT ANY WORK AND WE'RE ALL TOO SCARED TO GO HOME EARLY?

EXACTLY. I'VE READ ALL THE PAPERS ON-LINE, BOUGHT SOME CDs, CHECKED MY HOROSCOPE...

YAWN

email: alex-cartoon@etgate.co.uk

MANY BOSSES ARE NOW AFRAID TO PAY WOMEN LOWER BONUSES THAN MEN SINCE THIS RECENT SEX DISCRIMINATION COURT CASE...

I JUST TOLD AMANDA THE AMOUNT OF HER BONUS AND SHE REACTED IN A TYPICALLY FEMALE WAY. SOMETHING YOU'D NEVER SEE IN A MALE EMPLOYEE... THANKFULLY...

UNABLE TO HIDE HER DISAPPOINTMENT AT THE SUM SHE'D BEEN AWARDED, SHE RAN STRAIGHT TO THE LADIES' LOO AND HASN'T COME OUT YET. I'M VERY WORRIED.

THAT SHE'S IN THERE CRYING INCONSOLABLY?

NO, THAT SHE'S IN THERE EAVESDROPPING ON THE CONVERSATIONS OF THE SECRETARIES WHO TYPED THE BONUS LETTERS...

OH DEAR. SHE'LL FIND OUT WHAT EVERYONE ELSE GOT... THEN YOU'RE IN TROUBLE...

email: alex-cartoon@etgate.co.uk

I HEARD TODAY YOUR EX-COLLEAGUE JULIAN'S JUST BEEN MADE REDUNDANT FROM MEGABANK...

REALLY?

IT WAS VERY SUDDEN AND BRUTAL. HE ONLY GOT THE CONTRACTUAL MINIMUM OF ONE MONTH'S SALARY.

WELL THE BANKS ARE PLAYING TOUGH NOW THEY'VE REALISED THE DOWNTURN'S HERE TO STAY...

IT'S ONLY A FEW MONTHS SINCE YOU GOT MADE REDUNDANT FROM MEGABANK YOURSELF... MAYBE YOU AND JULIAN SHOULD GET TOGETHER AND COMMISERATE...

YES...THAT'S A NICE IDEA...

...WHEN THEY FIRED ME IN THE FIRST WAVE IN DECEMBER I GOT SIX MONTHS' MONEY... SO, JULIAN, HOW'S IT FEEL TO HAVE BEEN PAYING MEGABANK TO WORK FOR THEM?

OH SHUT UP...

email: alex-cartoon@etgate.co.uk

Alex
PEATTIE + TAYLOR
THE DEPUTY GOVERNOR OF THE BANK OF ENGLAND IS PREDICTING DIRE ECONOMIC CONSEQUENCES FROM THIS YEAR'S POOR CITY BONUSES...
APPARENTLY AVERAGE EARNINGS FOR THE WHOLE COUNTRY WILL BE LOWER AS A RESULT OF THE HARDSHIP IN THE FINANCIAL SECTOR...
WELL, THE AFFLUENT SOUTH EAST DRIVES MUCH OF THE ECONOMY.
OTHER SOCIAL GROUPS ARE BOUND TO FEEL THE KNOCK-ON EFFECT FROM THE ABSENCE OF MONEY IN THE STOCKBROKER BELT...
SUCH AS AN ABSENCE OF MONEY IN THE GARTER BELT?
QUITE. SOME OF MY CUSTOMERS HAVE BEEN REDUCED TO STICKING FIVERS IN MINE OF LATE...
PEPPERMINT HIPPO
STAFF ENTRANCE
email: alex-cartoon@etgate.co.uk

Alex
PEATTIE + TAYLOR
IT'S REFRESHING TO SEE YOU BACK IN A SUIT, STEVE.
WELL, ALEX, THE BANK'S REVERSED ITS DRESS DOWN POLICY...
WE WERE ONE OF THE FIRST ORGANISATIONS TO EMBRACE THE DOT.COM CULTURE AND ITS RELAXED DRESS CODE. SADLY THOUGH, THE NEW ECONOMY FAILED TO DELIVER THE PREDICTED PROFITS...
SO THE BANK HAS HAD TO CHANGE ITS BUSINESS FOCUS AND BY REVERTING TO MORE FORMAL BUSINESS DRESS CODE IS SENDING A CLEAR MESSAGE TO ITS STAFF...
"GET OUT AND DO SOME JOB INTERVIEWS AND SAVE US THE COST OF SACKING YOU"?
SOMETHING LIKE THAT... YES...
email: alex-cartoon@etgate.co.uk

Alex
PEATTIE + TAYLOR
WHEN THERE'S NO PROSPECT OF ANY DEALS WE BANKS RELY ON THE RETAINER FEES OUR CLIENTS PAY US, ROBIN...
BUT AT TIMES OF CUTBACKS CLIENTS OFTEN WANT TO DISCONTINUE THIS EXPENSE. WE MUST DISSUADE THEM FROM DOING SO... ALEX IS TALKING TO THE CHAIRMAN OF A CLIENT COMPANY NOW...
SIR ROGER,...
... ABOUT THE RETAINER YOU PAY TO KEEP MEGABANK AS YOUR ADVISERS. IT MUST BE VERY BURDENSOME FOR YOU, SO MY SUGGESTION IS THAT YOU STOP PAYING IT...
STOP THE RETAINER, SIR ROGER? THEY OBVIOUSLY WANT TO BE FREE TO WORK AGAINST US IN A HOSTILE TAKEOVER...
OH ****! LET'S OFFER THEM DOUBLE THE FEE IF THEY'LL STAY ON.
email: alex-cartoon@etgate.co.uk

Alex
PEATTIE + TAYLOR
DIVIDING UP THIS YEAR'S BONUS POOL HAS BEEN MADE HARDER BY THE SHORTAGE OF MONEY IN IT...
LUCKILY I'VE HAD A 100% SUCCESS RATE SO FAR IN PERSUADING THOSE PEOPLE ON GUARANTEED BONUSES TO RENOUNCE THEM. MARTIN JONES IS THE ONLY PERSON I HAVEN'T YET APPROACHED...
UNFORTUNATELY HE GOT WIND OF WHAT'S GOING ON AND CAME TO SEE ME YESTERDAY. HE SAID THAT NO WAY WAS HE GOING TO BE MY PATSY AND MAKE MY LIFE ANY EASIER...
OH DEAR...
SO HE RENOUNCED HIS GUARANTEE TOO?
DAMN. WE WERE PLANNING TO BLAME HIS GREED WHEN WE GAVE ZERO BONUSES TO EVERYONE ELSE...
NOW WE'LL HAVE TO ADMIT WE'VE PAID IT ALL TO OURSELVES.
email: alex-cartoon@etgate.co.uk

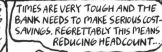

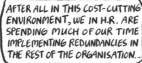

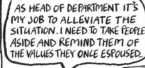

Alex FEATTIE + TAYLOR

THE MARKET DOWN-TURN HAS CREATED AN UNACCUSTOMED MOOD WITH EVERYONE FEELING DEFLATED AND INSECURE.....

AS HEAD OF DEPARTMENT IT'S MY JOB TO ALLEVIATE THE SITUATION. I NEED TO TAKE PEOPLE ASIDE AND REMIND THEM OF THE VALUES THEY ONCE ESPOUSED.

TO REKINDLE THE BULL MARKET SPIRIT THAT PERTAINED WHEN EVERYONE WAS WORKING HARD AND MAKING MONEY AND HAD THE IDEALISM AND ASSURANCE THAT WENT WITH IT...

REMEMBER HOW YOU USED TO GO ON ABOUT WORK/LIFE BALANCE ALEX, AND GRUMBLE ABOUT NEVER SEEING YOUR FAMILY?

FORGET IT... YOU'RE NOT GETTING ME TO SIGN UP FOR VOLUNTARY REDUNDANCY...

email: alex-cartoon@etgate.co.uk

Alex FEATTIE + TAYLOR

HEY, ALEX, HAND OVER YOUR SPONSORSHIP MONEY.

AH, SO YOU FINISHED THE LONDON MARATHON, TIM?

YES. I'M STIFF AND SORE BUT VERY FULFILLED. IT'S GOOD TO BE ABLE TO ACHIEVE A PERSONAL GOAL AND RAISE MONEY FOR CHARITY AT THE SAME TIME...

AN INSPIRATION TO US ALL...

IN FACT I'VE DECIDED TO BE MORE SOCIALLY RESPONSIBLE MYSELF AND DO SOME VOLUNTARY WORK... SO I'VE HAD MYSELF MADE DEPARTMENTAL FIRE WARDEN...

OH REALLY?

AH...THAT'LL BE THE FIRE DRILL I ORGANISED FOR THIS MORNING...

RRIIING

RRIIINGGG

SHUFFLE

LIMP

CREAK

COME ON, TIM. ONLY NINE FLOORS TO GO...

B*ST*RD!

email: alex-cartoon@etgate.co.uk

Alex FEATTIE + TAYLOR

WELCOME BACK, SARAH. HOW DID YOU ENJOY YOUR MATERNITY LEAVE?

IT WAS LOVELY THANKS, RUPERT...

AND FRANKLY WITH THE GRIM BUSINESS CLIMATE AND ALL THE DOWNSIZING IT WAS PROBABLY A GOOD TIME TO TAKE 3 MONTHS OUT OF THE MARKET. HOW'VE THINGS BEEN HERE?

MIXED, REALLY...

OBVIOUSLY THE BANK HAS HONOURED ITS LEGAL OBLIGATION TO KEEP YOUR JOB OPEN FOR YOU AND THE GOOD NEWS IS THAT WE'VE MADE YOU HEAD OF DEPARTMENT...

AND WHAT'S THE BAD NEWS?

ER... NO DEPARTMENT...

Alex FEATTIE + TAYLOR

ENGLAND V. ARGENTINA... IRELAND V GERMANY... SIGH

WHAT ARE YOU DOING, CLIVE?

LIKE EVERYONE I'D LOVE TO FIND AN EXCUSE TO GET OUT FOR THE WORLD CUP THIS SUMMER BUT RUPERT'S WISE TO IT AND HE'S ALREADY BANNED ALL BUSINESS TRAVEL TO JAPAN IN JUNE...

SO SADLY WE'LL ALL HAVE TO WATCH IT HERE ON T.V. AT HIGHLY INCONVENIENT HOURS OF THE DAY. I'M LISTING ALL THE IMPORTANT TIES I REALLY NEED TO SEE... ENGLAND V SWEDEN...

WHAT ABOUT YOU, ALEX?

THE SAME.

I'M LISTING ALL THE IMPORTANT THAIS I REALLY NEED TO SEE... BANGKOK'S IN A NEIGHBOURING TIME ZONE AND ONLY A SHORT HOP FROM JAPAN IF WE QUALIFY FOR THE 2ND STAGE...

ASIAN CLIENTS

email: alex-cartoon@etgate.co.uk

Alex — PEATTIE + TAYLOR

So Penny has no idea how dead the business climate is at the moment?

No, Clive.

I haven't told her. To be honest she'd only start to worry if she realised how fearful we all are for our bonuses, and indeed our jobs, right now...

She's not to know that we come into the bank every morning just to spend the whole day staring at our computer screens and trying to give the impression that we're working...

Another delivery from an on-line order service, Penny?

Yes: books, CDs, DVDs... This is bad news. Alex is clearly bored out of his skull at the office...

email: alex-cartoon@etgate.co.uk

Alex — PEATTIE + TAYLOR

The next round of redundancies — if necessary — would normally be at the end of June once the bank's half-yearly figures are in...

But business is so lamentable that frankly I might as well just call in the twenty people on my hit list and fire them right now...

What...?

Fire them now, when there's no need to? Rupert, have you really become so desensitised to others' feelings? Put yourself in their position... think what it'll mean to them

You're right, Alex...

They'd be able to sit at home and watch the whole of the world cup...

Exactly. Whereas getting the boot once it's all over will really hack them off

email: alex-cartoon@etgate.co.uk

Alex — PEATTIE + TAYLOR

So far the build-up to the world cup has been dominated by talk of injuries...

Yes

I suppose it was inevitable really that with a big tournament coming up there'd suddenly be question marks over the fitness of a few individuals.

And with England's group matches starting soon it seems likely that we'll have several members of the team missing for medical reasons

Yes...

...Justin's trying it on now...

I'll have to take the morning off on June 12th, Rupert. I've got a doctor's appointment about my back...

June 12th? Would that be the Nigeria game?

email: alex-cartoon@etgate.co.uk

Alex — PEATTIE + TAYLOR

Look, Damian, you're our junior food and drink analyst and somewhat new to the city...

Now, despite the fact that markets have been falling all year I notice that you haven't written a single "sell" recommendation on any stock...

This might suggest that, rather than being objective, your research is designed merely to suck up to the bank's corporate clients... have you ever heard of Chinese walls?

Well, no... I can't say I have...

What is it? Some far eastern ice cream franchise whose business you're pitching for? I'll rate it as a "buy"... Can I have some of your bonus if you win the deal?

email: alex-cartoon@etgate.co.uk

69

Alex PEATTIE + TAYLOR

OH NO! A SENIOR DIRECTOR FROM HEAD OFFICE IN NEW YORK IS FLYING IN UNEXPECTEDLY - TODAY OF ALL DAYS...

THE ENGLAND V ARGENTINA GAME KICKS OFF IN HALF AN HOUR AND JUST ABOUT EVERYBODY HAS SKIVED OFF TO WATCH IT. BUT BEING A YANK, HE WON'T HAVE A CLUE ABOUT SOCCER.

AND WE'VE GOT TO SHOW HIM ROUND A TRADING FLOOR MANNED BY A SKELETON STAFF OF PEOPLE WHO ARE NOT INTERESTED IN FOOTBALL, I.E. THE WOMEN. WHAT SORT OF IMPRESSION IS THAT GOING TO GIVE HIM?

AH, OKAY, SO I SEE YOU'VE FIRED ALL THE GUYS BUT HAD TO RETAIN THE WOMEN FOR P.C. REASONS... YEAH, IT'S THE SAME STORY BACK IN THE STATES... ER... QUITE. BLASTED MARKETS, EH?

email: alex-cartoon@etgate.co.uk

Alex PEATTIE + TAYLOR

DANNY WITTER IS ONE OF THE NEW BREED OF QUANTS WHO ARE TAKING OVER THE CITY THESE DAYS...

ONCE UPON A TIME IT WAS ENOUGH JUST TO INVITE OUR CLIENTS TO ASCOT IN ORDER TO GET THEM TO DEAL BUT NOW WE FIND OURSELVES MORE RELIANT ON THE MATHEMATICAL WHIZZERY OF THESE YOUNGSTERS...

WITH THEIR SPREADSHEETS AND COMPUTER MODELS AND COMPLEX ALGORITHMIC FORMULAE WHICH CAN TAKE INTO ACCOUNT MULTIPLE PARAMETERS AND VARIABLES... ALEX, I'VE GOT THOSE RESULTS FOR YOU...

UNLESS ENGLAND WIN THEIR GROUP AND THEN BEAT THE GROUP 'A' RUNNERS-UP - PROBABLY URUGUAY - THEIR QUARTER FINAL MATCH WON'T CLASH WITH ASCOT ON JUNE 22ND. AH GOOD. SO I CAN INVITE MY CLIENTS.

YES. NOW STOP WASTING MY TIME...

email: alex-cartoon@etgate.co.uk

Alex PEATTIE + TAYLOR

DOING THAT PITCH WAS A TOTAL WASTE OF TIME. NONE OF OUR CLIENTS SEEM TO WANT TO DEAL RIGHT NOW... GLOOM!

AT LEAST IT GOT US OUT OF THE OFFICE, CLIVE. THERE'S NOTHING MORE DEMORALISING THAN BEING COOPED UP THERE IN FRONT OF A DEALING SCREEN WATCHING THE MARKET GO NOWHERE...

AND DON'T FORGET THAT THE WORLD CUP IS NOW UNDERWAY. THIS GRAND EXHIBITION OF THE FOOT-BALLING SKILLS OF 32 NATIONS FROM ACROSS THE GLOBE SHOULD HOPEFULLY BRIGHTEN OUR MOOD...

SEE?... THAT PUB'S PACKED OUT FOR CAMEROON V SAUDI ARABIA... BRIGHTEN

PHEW! CLEARLY NOBODY ELSE HAS GOT ANY WORK ON EITHER...

WORLD CUP TODAY 10. AM

email: alex-cartoon@etgate.co.uk

Alex PEATTIE + TAYLOR

SO, RUPERT, YOU DECIDED TO SCREEN TODAY'S WORLD CUP FIXTURE IN THE BANK?

WELL, SO MANY PEOPLE WERE DREDGING UP BOGUS DENTAL APPOINTMENTS AND WASHING MACHINE DELIVERIES THAT FRANKLY IT WAS EASIER JUST TO GIVE IN...

SO WE'VE SUPPLIED COFFEE AND CROISSANTS AND A PLAMSA T.V. SCREEN FOR TODAY'S 7.30 KICK-OFF. I'M PLEASED TO SAY WE'VE GOT A 100% TURN-OUT...

SO MUCH FOR THOSE STAFF WHO CLAIM THEY'RE PHYSICALLY UNABLE TO GET IN BEFORE 8.30 DUE TO RAIL CONNECTIONS.. MORNING MEETINGS WILL BE AT 7.15 IN FUTURE.

email: alex-cartoon@etgate.co.uk

Alex *PEATTIE + TAYLOR*

IT'S THE WORLD CUP QUARTER FINAL BETWEEN ENGLAND AND BRAZIL AND THERE'S NO WAY WE CAN STOP STAFF WATCHING IT...

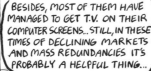

BESIDES, MOST OF THEM HAVE MANAGED TO GET T.V. ON THEIR COMPUTER SCREENS... STILL, IN THESE TIMES OF DECLINING MARKETS AND MASS REDUNDANCIES IT'S PROBABLY A HELPFUL THING...

OBVIOUSLY A BIG ROAR GOES UP ROUND THE TRADING ROOM EVERY TIME ENGLAND GET THE BALL... BUT NOW IT'S BRAZIL ON THE ATTACK...

OLÉ!

AND A LONE CHEER RINGS OUT...

HMM... ODD... I THOUGHT WE SACKED OUR LATIN AMERICAN EQUITIES TEAM LAST WEEK... MUST'VE MISSED SOMEONE. FIND HIM AND FIRE HIM, WOULD YOU?

email: alex-cartoon@etgate.co.uk

Alex *PEATTIE + TAYLOR*

ANOTHER TEN PERCENT HEADCOUNT REDUCTION HAS BEEN ORDERED ON A "LAST IN, FIRST OUT" BASIS...

≥ SIGH ≥

HOW CAN MY DEPARTMENT DO ITS JOB EFFECTIVELY - I.E. RESEARCHING POTENTIAL TAKEOVER TARGETS ON BEHALF OF OUR CORPORATE CLIENTS WITH THESE LATEST PERSONNEL CUTS?

WELL, TO BE HONEST, RUPERT, THE BANK IS JUST GETTING RID OF DEAD WOOD AND IS SACKING THE SURPLUS STAFF WE ACCUMULATED DURING THE BOOM YEARS...

EXACTLY.

WHICH NOW CONSTITUTES EVERY SINGLE EMPLOYEE FROM THE RIVAL BANK WE BOUGHT LAST YEAR FOR ¥6 BN...

AH YES... HARDLY A SHINING EXAMPLE OF OUR WISDOM IN THE FIELD OF CORPORATE TAKEOVERS.

email: alex-cartoon@etgate.co.uk

Alex *PEATTIE + TAYLOR*

I'M SORRY... I'M GOING TO HAVE TO CALL THE WHOLE THING OFF... I'VE BEEN A FOOL... I SHOULD HAVE KNOWN IT WOULD NEVER WORK OUT...

THANK GOODNESS MY GIRLFRIEND NEVER SUSPECTED WHAT WAS GOING ON... OH GOD, SHE'S COMING... LOOK, I HAVE TO GO... PLEASE DON'T CALL ME ON THIS NUMBER AGAIN...

WHO WAS THAT YOU WERE TALKING TO, CLIVE?

OH... ER, NO ONE, BRIDGET... I MEAN ... ER, IT WAS A WRONG NUMBER...

ANOTHER ONE FURTIVELY CANCELLING HIS PROVISIONAL BOOKING TO JAPAN FOR JUNE 30TH

MEN! ... THEY REALLY BELIEVED ENGLAND MIGHT MAKE IT TO THE WORLD CUP FINAL...

TRAVEL AGENT

FLORIDA
BRITISH AIRWAYS
JAPAN

CLICK

email: alex-cartoon@etgate.co.uk

Alex *PEATTIE + TAYLOR*

I HEAR THE BANK'S HAD TO SHED TWO OF ITS ECONOMISTS...

YES. HEAD OFFICE HAS BEEN DEMANDING MORE CUTS...

IN THIS WORSENING CLIMATE IT WAS HARD TO KNOW WHO TO GET RID OF. THOUGH MANY BANKERS DREAM OF ESCAPING THE CITY, FEW OF US HAVE SKILLS TRANSFERABLE TO THE REAL WORLD...

HOWEVER GORDON HAS BEEN HARPING ON ABOUT OPENING AN ART GALLERY AND PATRICK HAS ACTIVE PLANS TO SET UP A WINE IMPORTING BUSINESS, SO THEY SEEMED THE OBVIOUS REDUNDANCY CANDIDATES...

BECAUSE THEY CLEARLY UNDERSTAND NOTHING ABOUT ECONOMICS?

EXACTLY. DO THE IDIOTS REALLY THINK ANYONE'S GOING TO HAVE MONEY TO SPEND ON PAINTINGS OR FINE WINES THE WAY THE STOCK MARKET'S GOING?

MEGA BANK

Alex PEATTIE + TAYLOR

FIRST ENRON, NOW WORLDCOM... AND WHO KNOWS HOW MANY OTHER COMPANIES COULD SECRETLY BE HIDING HUGE LOSSES?

I HOPE THE DIRECTORS RESPONSIBLE FOR THESE COVER UPS GET THE HEFTY PRISON SENTENCES THEY DESERVE. AFTER ALL, THEIR SELFISH ACTIONS HAVE RUINED OTHER PEOPLE'S LIVES...

I'M TALKING ABOUT THE HARD-WORKING INDIVIDUALS WHO'D BEEN LOOKING FORWARD TO A COMFORTABLE RETIREMENT AND NOW FIND THEIR DREAMS OF FINANCIAL SECURITY IN OLD AGE DASHED...

THE WORLDCOM EMPLOYEES?

NO... SENIOR BANKERS LIKE ME... A FEW NON-EXECUTIVE DIRECTORSHIPS WERE ONCE A COSY SINECURE FOR OUR TWILIGHT YEARS, BUT NOW WE COULD END UP TAKING THE FLAK FOR SOMETHING LIKE THIS...

email: alex-cartoon@etgate.co.uk

Alex PEATTIE + TAYLOR

I'VE JUST FOUND OUT THAT ALEX HAS TO GO INTO HOSPITAL FOR AN OPERATION TOMORROW...

YOU MEAN HE DIDN'T TELL YOU?

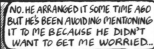

NO. HE ARRANGED IT SOME TIME AGO BUT HE'S BEEN AVOIDING MENTIONING IT TO ME BECAUSE HE DIDN'T WANT TO GET ME WORRIED...

IT LOOKS LIKE YOU _ARE_ WORRIED, PENNY...

HOW COULD I NOT BE? ESPECIALLY WHEN HE TOLD ME THE SERIOUSNESS OF THE MEDICAL CONDITION HE'S BEING OPERATED ON FOR...

OH MY GOD! WHAT?

A MINOR LIGAMENT NIGGLE HE PICKED UP PLAYING RUGBY 15 YEARS AGO...

OH NO... IF HE'S SUDDENLY TAKING ADVANTAGE OF THE BANK'S PRIVATE HEALTH PLAN HE MUST THINK HE'S ABOUT TO BE SACKED.

email: alex-cartoon@etgate.co.uk

Alex PEATTIE + TAYLOR

A FEMALE EX-EMPLOYEE IS SUING THE BANK BECAUSE SHE RECEIVED SMALLER BONUSES THAN HER MALE COLLEAGUES...

NOW THE PLAIN TRUTH IS THAT WE FELT SHE WASN'T UP TO HER JOB – HENCE THE LOWER BONUSES – YET SHE'S PORTRAYING IT AS SEXUAL DISCRIMINATION AND CLAIMING £5M IN DAMAGES...

I'M SHELL-SHOCKED. I HAD NO IDEA SHE COULD BE CAPABLE OF SUCH SELF-SERVING, VINDICTIVE, BARE-FACED DUPLICITOUS, EGOTISTICAL UTTERLY UNPRINCIPLED GREED

ME NEITHER...

I VOTE WE OFFER HER HER JOB BACK...

HEAR HEAR. THESE ARE JUST THE SORT OF BALLSY QUALITIES WE LOOK FOR...

email: alex-cartoon@etgate.co.uk

Alex PEATTIE + TAYLOR

ONCE UPON A TIME THE IDEA OF LIVING IN THE 21ST CENTURY SEEMED SO FUTURISTIC AND MYSTICAL BUT LIFE HASN'T CHANGED.

THINK OF THE POP SONGS THAT WERE WRITTEN ABOUT THE MILLENNIUM – YOU KNOW, LIKE BY PRINCE AND ROBBIE WILLIAMS – THEY'RE ALREADY OBSOLETE...

WHEREAS A GREAT LOVE SONG IS TIMELESS, THOSE MILLENNIUM ANTHEMS DON'T MEAN ANYTHING TO ANYONE ANY MORE. I MEAN WHO'S GOING TO BOTHER LISTENING TO THEM TODAY?

♪ TONIGHT WE'RE GONNA PARTY LIKE IT'S NINETEEN NINETY-NINE... ♪

AH... REMEMBER 1999, CLIVE? THE LAST YEAR OF MEGA-BONUSES?

AND THE PARTIES WE HAD...! VINTAGE CHAMPAGNE, HELICOPTERS TO MONTE CARLO...

email: alex-cartoon@etgate.co.uk

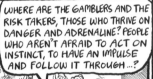

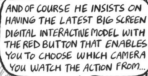

OTHER ALEX BOOKS

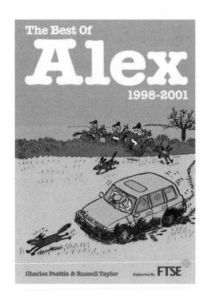

THE BEST OF ALEX 1998-2001

Covering four years of life in the City of London that saw the full Bust to Boom and Back Again economic cycle: the collapse of Russia and the Far East in 1998; the dotcom bubble; the non-event that was the Y2K bug; the predictable yet unpredicted burst of the dotcom bubble; and the revision to familiar recessionary habits in 2001.

£9.99 (plus p&p)

THE ALEX TECHNIQUE

Here for the first time, Alex shares some of the tricks of the trade that have kept him at the top in the world of international finance.

£7.99 (plus p&p)

Also from Masterley Publishing: CELEB by Charles Peattie and Mark Warren

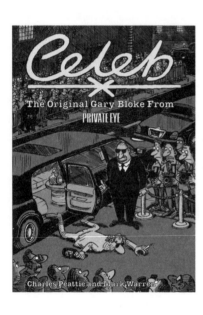

"Celeb", the long running cartoon strip from the pages of Private Eye, featuring the private life of Gary Bloke - the ultimate wrinkly rock star.

£9.99 (plus p&p)

Cartoon Originals and Prints

The Alex and Celeb cartoon strip originals are all for sale. A strip measures 4x14 inches. If there's a particular one you want, phone or email us some information about it (the date it appeared, what the punch line was etc.) and we'll let you know if we still have it. If the original is not available, or you are too mean to purchase it, we can make a print of it for you. Originals and prints are signed by the creators.

For further details on details on prices and delivery please call 01371 831846.

Originals, prints and books are available from:

Alex
Orchard End,
Watling Lane
Thaxted
CM6 2QY

Tel. 01371 831846
Fax. 01371 831847
Email alex-cartoon@etgate.co.uk

WWW.ALEXCARTOON.COM